TEENAGE MUTANT NINJA TURTLES
BOOK II

Kevin Eastman and Peter Laird

Steve Lavigne
LETTERS and COLORS

FIRST
GRAPHIC NOVEL

Teenage Mutant Ninja Turtles®: Book II
First Graphic Novel Number Ten

Published by First Publishing, Inc.
435 N. LaSalle, Chicago IL 60610

ISBN: 0-915419-22-X

First Printing: June, 1987
Second Printing: June, 1988
Third Printing: March, 1989

4 5 6 7 8 9 0

Printed in the United States of America

Rick Obadiah, Publisher   Larry Doyle, Managing Editor
Kathy Kotsivas, Operations Director   Laurel Fitch, Editor
Ralph C. Musicant, Financial Director   Alex Wald, Art Director
Kurt Goldzung, Sales Director   Michael McCormick, Production Manager
Rich Markow, Editorial Coordinator

TEENAGE MUTANT NINJA TURTLES
BOOK II

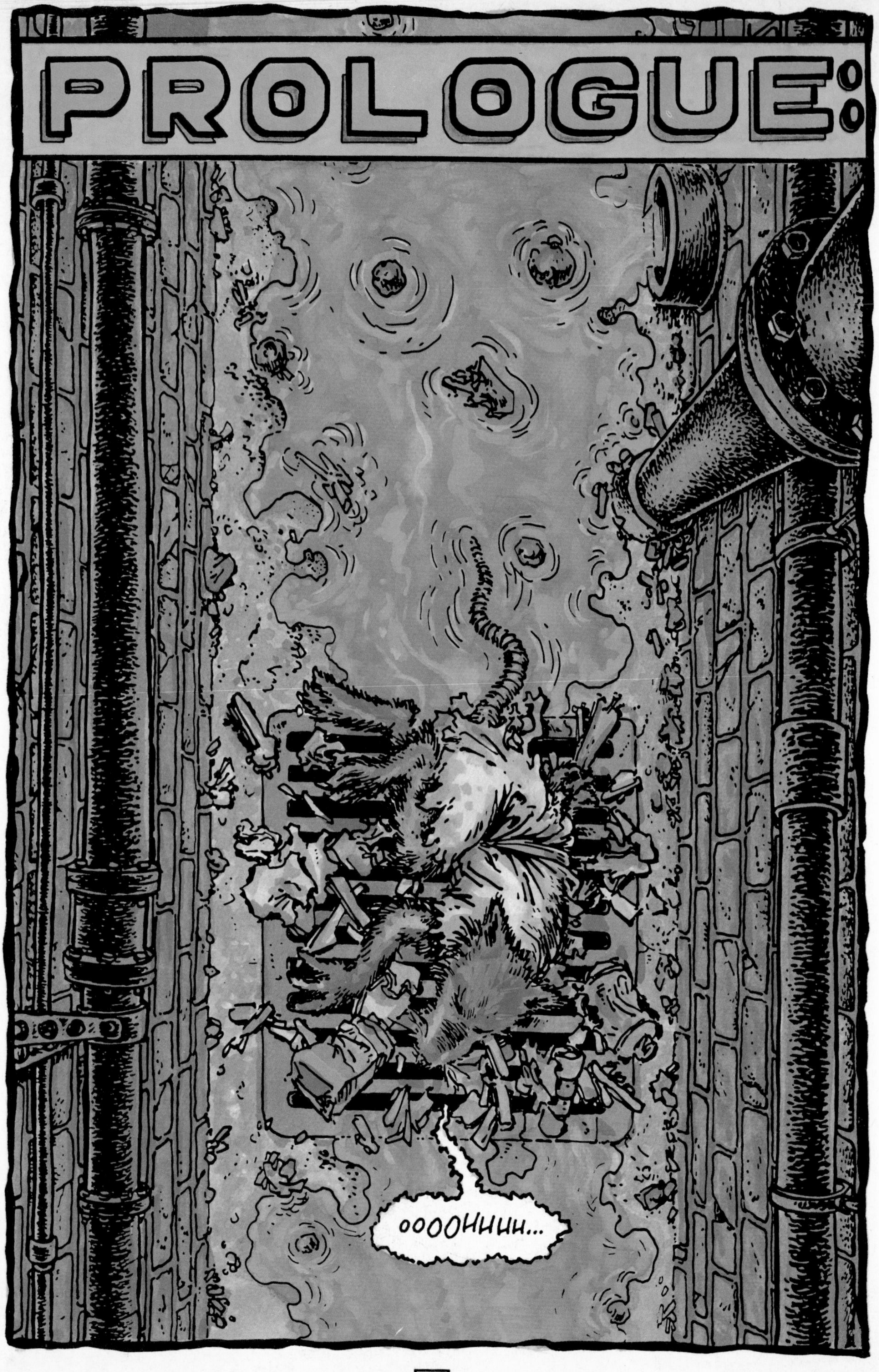
PROLOGUE:
OOOOHHHH...

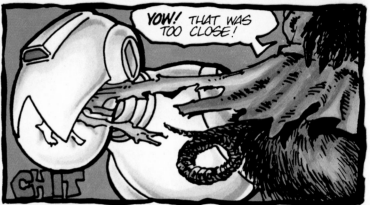

4

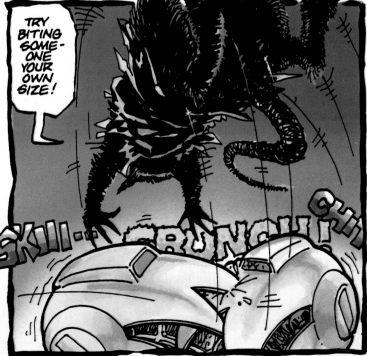

GOT TO...

GLUB.

GOT TO GET... AWAY...

...GET AWAY...
...BEFORE THEY...
...COME BACK...

UNH... MY HEAD THROBBING.. W-WHAT'S THAT *NOISE*...? MOUSERS...?

THIS IS ONE PART OF OUR DUTY THAT I DO NOT ENJOY...

THE ROTTING SMELL... IT IS TERRIBLE.

TCRI

I AGREE. BUT THIS DRAIN GRATE NEEDS TO BE KEPT CLEAR.

OBSERVE... ANOTHER HALF-DEAD RODENT.

APPARENTLY THAT STOCKMAN PERSON'S PLAN WAS NOT COMPLETELY SUCCESSFUL.

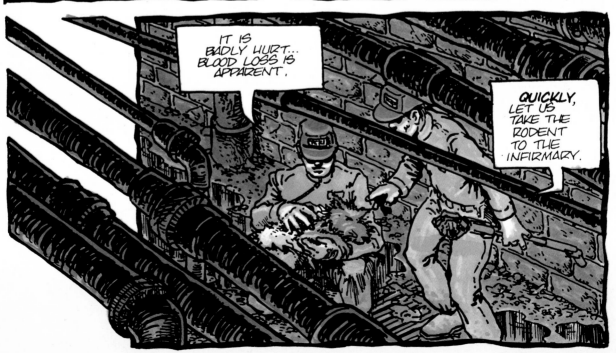

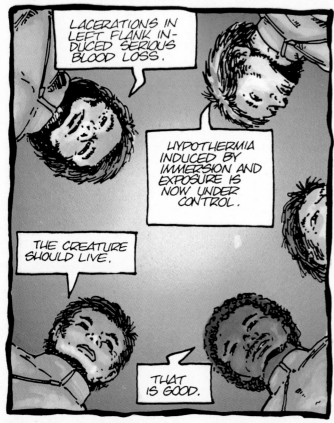

TEENAGE MUTANT NINJA TURTLES!

I'M GLAD THAT MIKE AND RAPHAEL THOUGHT OF THIS... NOT ONLY IS THE EXERTION A WELCOME DIVERSION...

...BUT IT'S A BEAUTIFUL NIGHT TO BE OUT IN! THAT COOL BREEZE BLOWING IN OFF THE OCEAN...

...IT'S CARRYING AWAY SOME OF THIS NEW YORK CITY SMOG. FOR ONCE, THE AIR IS ALMOST CLEAR!

ALLEZ--

BEAUTIFUL! GREAT FLIP MIKE!

--OOP!

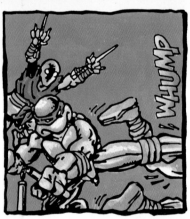

...FOR THE SHREDDER!
TAK
NO...
TAK
THUNK
--"FOR SPLINTER"!
HAH! YOU CAST AWAY YOUR BO*!
NOW YOU STAND ALONE AND WEAPONLESS--
--AGAINST THREE OF US! NOW DIE!!!
YOUR OVERCONFIDENCE BETRAYS YOU--
--FOR I AM A NINJA TURTLE, AND MY BEST WEAPONS--
* STAFF

21

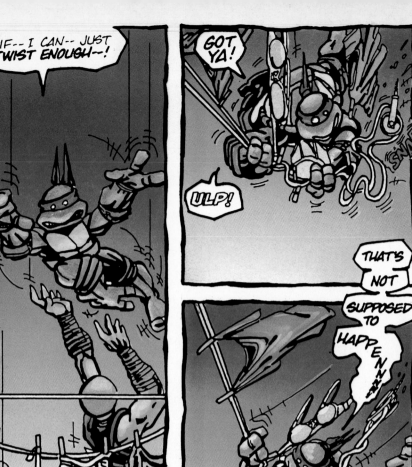

YAAA!

OH WOW...

WHAT A LANDING!

UH... HI THERE! SORRY ABOUT YOUR... AH ...WINDOW... UM...

AH... BETTER BE GOING NOW!

SLAM!

MOMMA-- WHO WAS THAT LITTLE GREEN MAN?

25

THEN THEY ALL SEE IT...

...AND FOUR TURTLES SHARE THE SAME **SHOCK** OF **RECOGNITION**...

...THE LETTERS **TCRI** LEAP OUT OF THEIR MEMORIES...

...AS THEY RECALL THEIR ORIGIN AS RELATED TO THEM BY SPLINTER!

OF THAT DAY FIFTEEN YEARS AGO... A SPEEDING TRUCK ON A POTHOLED STREET... A HEROIC ACT BY A YOUNG BOY...

A METAL CANNISTER, JARRED OUT OF THE TRUCK, BOUNCING ON THE STREET... SMASHING A BOWL HOLDING FOUR SMALL **TURTLES**...

...THE TURTLES AND THE CANNISTER FALLING INTO AN OPEN MANHOLE... THE CANISTER BREAKING OPEN, RELEASING A GLOWING **OOZE**...

...THE YOUNG TURTLES, STUNNED BUT ALIVE, CRAWLING AROUND IN THAT OOZE... AND THE CHANGES BEGAN!

28

THAT'S VERY *STRANGE*...

I HOPE THOSE STITCHES HOLD, MIKE -- THAT'S A PRETTY BAD SLASH...

WHAT'S STRANGE, DONATELLO?

THERE'S NO LISTING IN THE PHONE BOOK OR IN INFORMATION... AND THE CHAMBER OF COMMERCE HAS NEVER HEARD OF *TCRI!*

UMM... MUST BE A *C.I.A.* FRONT OR SOMETHING...

...OR A TOP SECRET WEAPONS LAB!

WHAT IS?

TCRI!

OH YEAH?

ABOUT TIME YOU GOT OUT OF THE SHOWER, RAPHAEL! THERE'D BETTER BE SOME HOT WATER LEFT!

DON'T SWEAT IT, *BIG BOY!*

OW! HEY!

SNAP

KNOCK KNOCK

THEY **AMBUSHED** US -- ABOUT **TWENTY** OF THEM! CUT MIKE'S ARM UP PRETTY BAD... BUT WE TOOK CARE OF THEM!

OOH, **LEO** -- YOUR CUT LOOKS PRETTY AWFUL, TOO! HERE, GIVE ME THAT **PEROXIDE**!

WHERE'D YOU RUN INTO THOSE GUYS -- AROUND HERE?

OW!

NO, OVER IN **BROOKLYN**. WE GOT 'EM ALL... I DON'T THINK WE WERE FOLLOWED BACK HERE.

I SHUDDER TO THINK WHAT MIGHT HAPPEN IF THEY FOUND OUT WHERE WE LIVED!

BUT -- THAT'S NOT THE **REALLY** BIG NEWS!

DON, GO GET THE **DISPLAY CASE**...

HE'S RIGHT... WAIT 'TIL YOU HEAR THIS!

DO YOU REMEMBER THE *TCRI* CANNISTER, APRIL?

I--I DON'T THINK I EVER SAW IT, BUT I DO REMEMBER SPLINTER TELLING ME ABOUT IT...

...WASN'T THIS CANNISTER THE SOURCE OF THE MYSTERIOUS "GOO" WHICH CAUSED YOU TO *MUTATE*?

RIGHT YOU ARE! WELL, AFTER ALL THIS TIME, WE HAVE A LEAD ON THIS "TCRI" COMPANY -- WHILE FIGHTING THE "FOOT" WE STUMBLED ONTO A BUILDING BEARING THAT SAME *LOGO*!

WE'RE GOING BACK TONIGHT TO CHECK IT OUT... EVEN THOUGH IT MEANS INTERRUPTING OUR SEARCH FOR SPLINTER!

HE'D UNDERSTAND, THOUGH. THE CHANCE TO KNOW WHY WE ARE WHAT WE ARE -- IT'S JUST TOO IMPORTANT TO PASS UP!

I WANT TO COME WITH YOU...

THANKS... BUT NO, APRIL--

--YOU CAN'T COME. IT'S TOO *DANGEROUS*... NOT TO MENTION *ILLEGAL*!

WE MUST GO -- THE ANSWERS WE MIGHT FIND ARE THAT MEANINGFUL!

LATER THAT NIGHT...

I DON'T SEE ANY SIDE DOORS OR WINDOWS-- THIS PLACE IS STRANGE!

MIKE'S SCOUTING THE BACK--

HEY, GUESS WHAT--?

--ZIP! NOT A DOOR, WINDOW, LEDGE, OR ANYTHING!

THEN HOW DO WE GET IN? WE CAN'T GO THROUGH THE FRONT DOOR--AND MIKE CAN'T CLIMB ALL THE WAY TO THE TOP WITH THAT ARM WOUND!

I'VE GOT IT! WATCH THIS--!

EEE...

OH, I SEE! WE GO UP TO THE ROOF OF THIS BUILDING...

YAH!

...THEN CROSS OVER! BUT WAIT-- WHAT IF THAT DOOR HAS AN--

SHRAK

ALARM?

33

OH, I SEE-- THESE **ELECTRIC EYES** TAKE UP THE *SLACK!*

THE CAMERA'S JUST A SMALL PROBLEM-- THOSE EYES WILL REQUIRE SOME FANCY FOOT-WORK!

FIRST, AN INSTANT PHOTO OF THE AREA SCANNED BY THE CAMERA--

CLICK

--THEN ATTACH IT TO THIS HOLDER-- AND FOR MY LAST TRICK, TO GET THE PHOTO IN FRONT OF THE LENS WITHOUT BEING SEEN--

HERE GOES NOTHING--!

AT A SECURITY STATION WITHIN THE TCRI BUILDING...

ANOTHER PIGEON BLOCKING THE ROOF CAMERA--THIS CITY IS INFESTED WITH THEM!

OK GUY'S-- C'MON OVER!

NOW WE CAN WALK RIGHT IN FRONT OF IT.

--BUT BE CAREFUL TO WALK WHERE I TELL YOU TO-- THESE ELECTRIC EYES ARE VERY SENSITIVE!

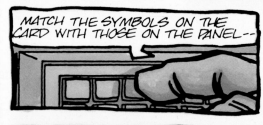

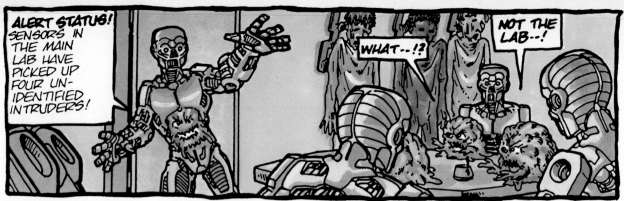

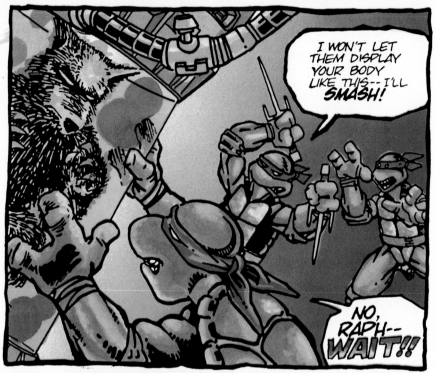

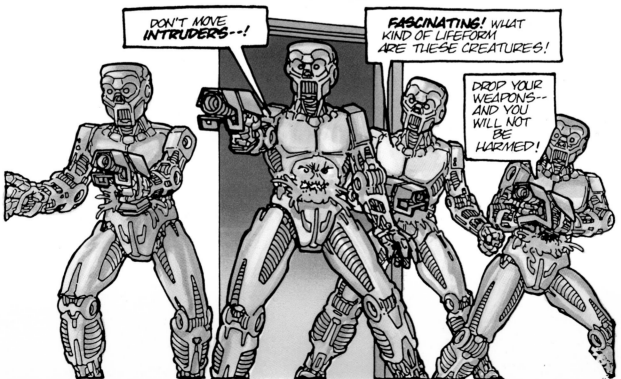

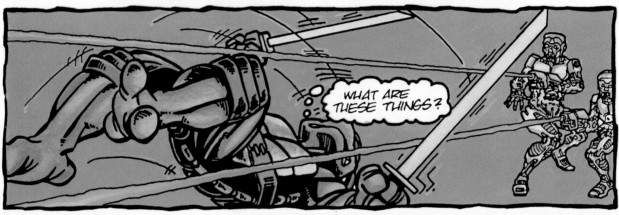

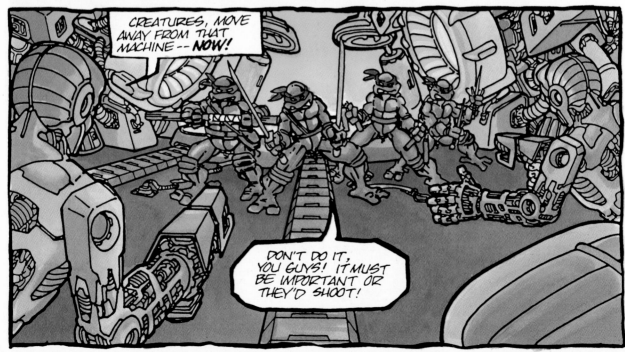

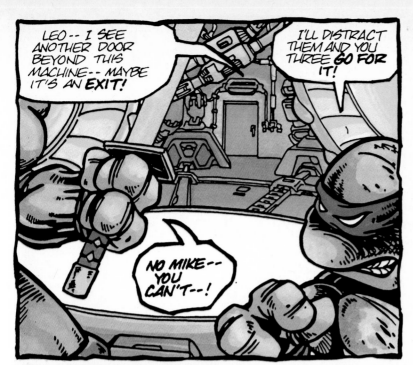

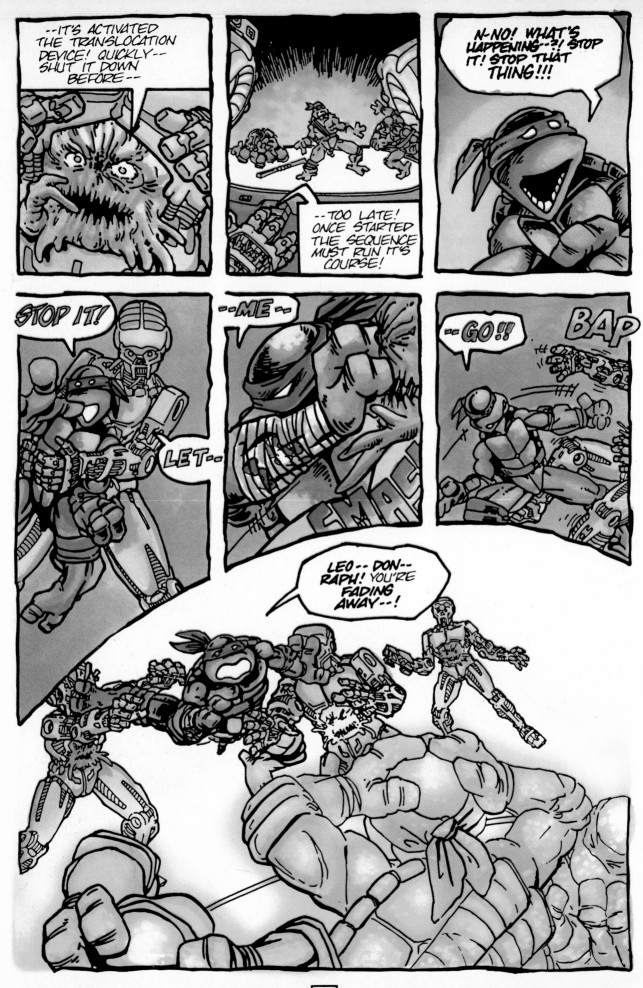

MY WORD! THOSE FELLOWS ARE MAKING SHORT WORK OF THESE TROOPS-- BUT MORE ARE BOUND TO SHOW UP!

HMM... THIS WALL...

AHA! IT IS WOOD!

AND MAYBE WEAK ENOUGH FOR ME TO DO--

--THIS!

CRACK

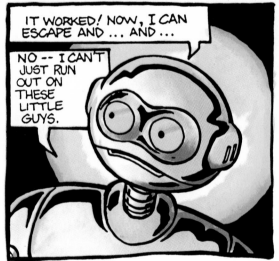

IT WORKED! NOW, I CAN ESCAPE AND ... AND ...

NO -- I CAN'T JUST RUN OUT ON THESE LITTLE GUYS.

HEY-- YOU GUYS-- OVER HERE!

THIS WAY, QUICKLY!

OH, NO-- HERE COME SOME MORE OF THOSE GOONS!

AND THIS IS A DEAD END ALLEY-- DAMN!!!

HUH? HEY, LEO-- LOOK!

A WAY OUT!

WOW--THIS IS A WEIRD CITY, MAN!

CHECK OUT THOSE DUDES!

WHERE?

OH, MY GOD...

...WHERE THE HECK...

...ARE WE?

...AND I THOUGHT NEW YORK WAS STRANGE!

SEVERAL MINUTES AND A FEW MILES LATER...

I CAN'T SEE ANY SIGNS OF PURSUIT...

...AND THIS LOOKS LIKE A GOOD SECTION OF TOWN TO HIDE OUT IN!

LET'S GO!

HOPE WE CAN FIND A SHOWER OR SOMETHING, YUCK!

SO, UH... WHO ARE YOU AND WHERE ARE WE?

YOU'RE IN THE CITY OF PEBLAK, OF COURSE! AS FOR ME...

...MY STORY IS LONG AND SHOULD WAIT 'TIL WE'RE WELL HIDDEN!

HMM...THIS ONE SHOULD DO...

FOR WHAT?

THIS, MY BOYS, IS HOME FOR AWHILE!

EARTH? IS THAT YOUR HOME PLANET?

HOME PLANET..?! WHAT'S THIS "HOME PLANET" CRAP!!

WHAT ARE YOU TRYING TO TELL US?!!!

CALM DOWN, SON -- FIRST OF ALL, I'VE NEVER HEARD OF EARTH. SECOND, YOU ARE RIGHT NOW ON THE PLANET D'HOONIB IN THE SIDAYOM SYSTEM, FEDERATION TERRITORY.

OH, AND MY NAME IS HONEYCUTT.

I WANT TO THANK YOU FELLOWS FOR HELPING ME OUT BACK THERE...

...AND VICE VERSA.... UH... HONEYCUTT! BY THE WAY, I'M LEONARDO!

RAPHAEL!

MICHAELANGELO!

DONATELLO!

WHAT I'D LIKE TO KNOW IS: HOW'D WE GET HERE, AND HOW DO WE GET BACK HOME? IT SEEMS LIKE JUST MINUTES AGO THAT WE HAD FOUND OUR MASTER, SPLINTER, IN THE T.C.R.I. LAB, AND WERE FIGHTING TO RESCUE HIM FROM HIS WEIRD CAPTORS...

...AND WE RETREATED INTO A ROOM NEAR A....A...TRANSLOCATION DEVICE, I THINK THEY CALLED IT. NEXT THING I KNOW, WE'RE IN AN ALLEY WITH YOU AND THOSE GOONS!

A WHAT--?

WHAT KIND OF DEVICE?

A TRANSLOCATION DEVICE -- YOU KNOW WHAT THAT IS?

HMM... VERY INTERESTING... YES, I SEE... IT ADDS UP...

WHAT DO YOU MEAN?

IF I'M RIGHT, YOU WERE CAUGHT IN THE BEAM MATRIX OF A TRANSMAT MACHINE -- A DEVICE WHICH INSTANTANEOUSLY TRANSMITS MATTER OVER VAST DISTANCES. SOMEHOW, IT SENT YOU HERE!

I WAS WORKING ON A SIMILAR DEVICE BEFORE --

YOU WERE?! THEN YOU CAN GET US BACK HOME --?!

YEAH!

LET'S GET STARTED!

HOLD ON NOW -- IT'S NOT THAT SIMPLE...

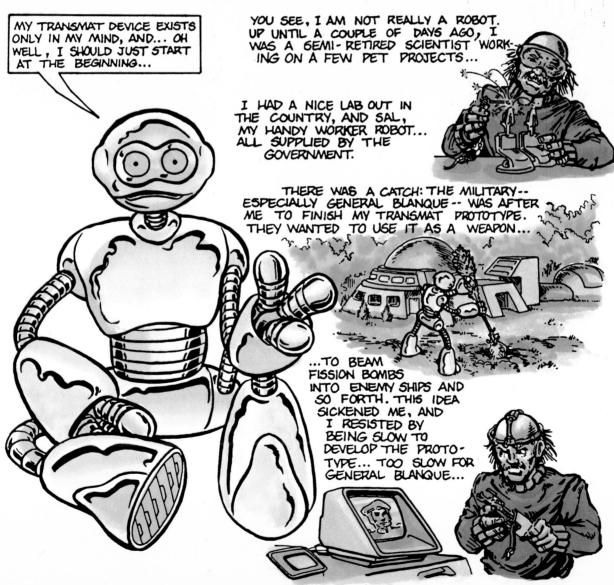

MY TRANSMAT DEVICE EXISTS ONLY IN MY MIND, AND... OH WELL, I SHOULD JUST START AT THE BEGINNING...

YOU SEE, I AM NOT REALLY A ROBOT. UP UNTIL A COUPLE OF DAYS AGO, I WAS A SEMI-RETIRED SCIENTIST WORKING ON A FEW PET PROJECTS...

I HAD A NICE LAB OUT IN THE COUNTRY, AND SAL, MY HANDY WORKER ROBOT... ALL SUPPLIED BY THE GOVERNMENT.

THERE WAS A CATCH: THE MILITARY -- ESPECIALLY GENERAL BLANQUE -- WAS AFTER ME TO FINISH MY TRANSMAT PROTOTYPE. THEY WANTED TO USE IT AS A WEAPON...

...TO BEAM FISSION BOMBS INTO ENEMY SHIPS AND SO FORTH. THIS IDEA SICKENED ME, AND I RESISTED BY BEING SLOW TO DEVELOP THE PROTOTYPE... TOO SLOW FOR GENERAL BLANQUE...

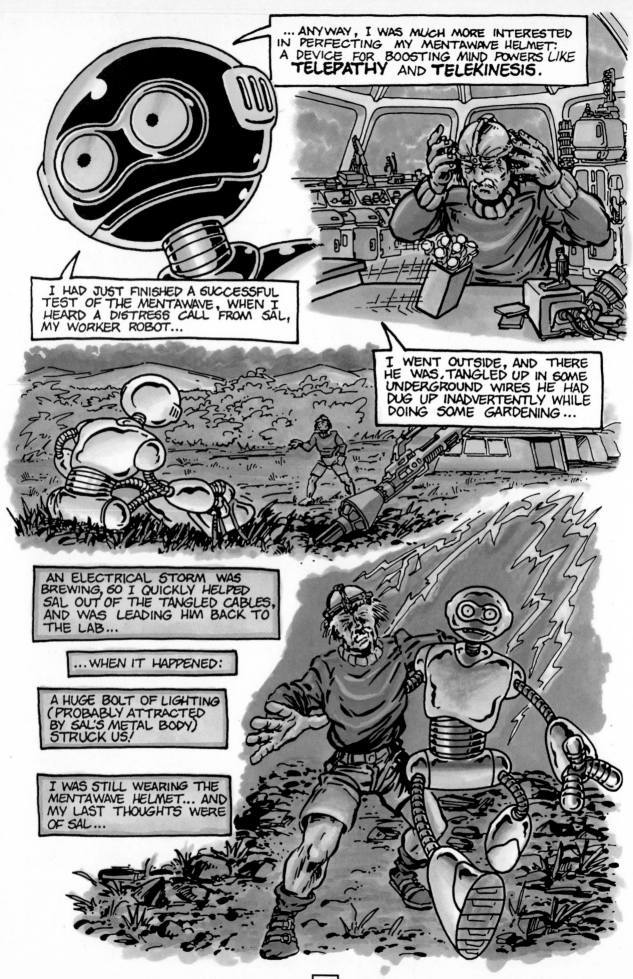

...ANYWAY, I WAS MUCH MORE INTERESTED IN PERFECTING MY MENTAWAVE HELMET: A DEVICE FOR BOOSTING MIND POWERS LIKE **TELEPATHY** AND **TELEKINESIS.**

I HAD JUST FINISHED A SUCCESSFUL TEST OF THE MENTAWAVE, WHEN I HEARD A DISTRESS CALL FROM SAL, MY WORKER ROBOT...

I WENT OUTSIDE, AND THERE HE WAS, TANGLED UP IN SOME UNDERGROUND WIRES HE HAD DUG UP INADVERTENTLY WHILE DOING SOME GARDENING...

AN ELECTRICAL STORM WAS BREWING, SO I QUICKLY HELPED SAL OUT OF THE TANGLED CABLES, AND WAS LEADING HIM BACK TO THE LAB...

...WHEN IT HAPPENED:

A HUGE BOLT OF LIGHTING (PROBABLY ATTRACTED BY SAL'S METAL BODY) STRUCK US!

I WAS STILL WEARING THE MENTAWAVE HELMET... AND MY LAST THOUGHTS WERE OF SAL...

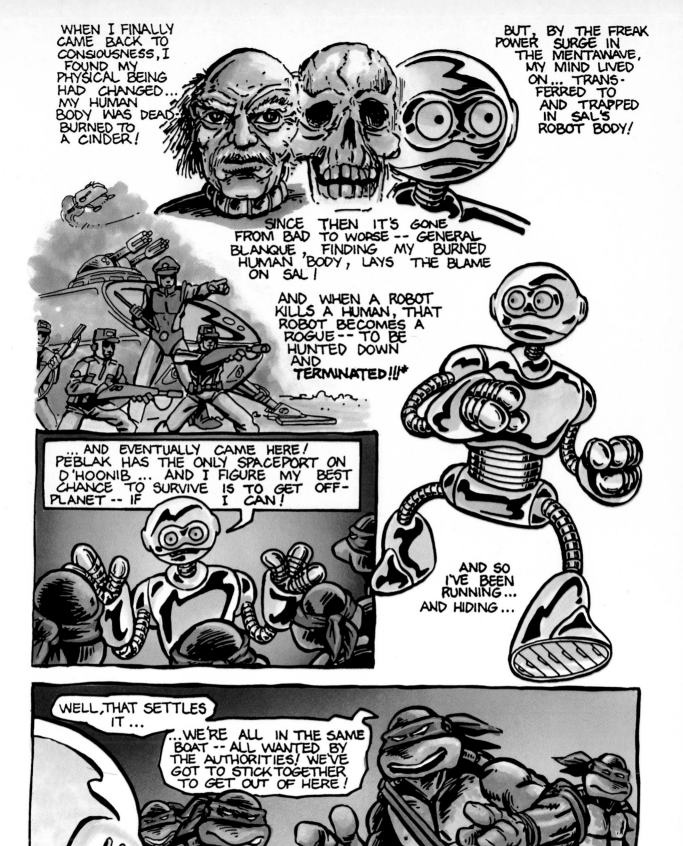

WHEN I FINALLY CAME BACK TO CONSIOUSNESS, I FOUND MY PHYSICAL BEING HAD CHANGED... MY HUMAN BODY WAS DEAD-- BURNED TO A CINDER!

BUT, BY THE FREAK POWER SURGE IN THE MENTAWAVE, MY MIND LIVED ON ... TRANSFERRED TO AND TRAPPED IN SAL'S ROBOT BODY!

SINCE THEN IT'S GONE FROM BAD TO WORSE -- GENERAL BLANQUE, FINDING MY BURNED HUMAN 'BODY, LAYS THE BLAME ON SAL!

AND WHEN A ROBOT KILLS A HUMAN, THAT ROBOT BECOMES A ROGUE -- TO BE HUNTED DOWN AND TERMINATED!!!*

...AND EVENTUALLY CAME HERE! PEBLAK HAS THE ONLY SPACEPORT ON D'HOONIB ... AND I FIGURE MY BEST CHANCE TO SURVIVE IS TO GET OFF-PLANET -- IF I CAN!

AND SO I'VE BEEN RUNNING... AND HIDING...

WELL, THAT SETTLES IT ...

...WE'RE ALL IN THE SAME BOAT -- ALL WANTED BY THE AUTHORITIES! WE'VE GOT TO STICK TOGETHER TO GET OUT OF HERE!

* OF COURSE HONEYCUTT DOESN'T KNOW THAT GENERAL BLANQUE IS NOW AWARE OF HIS "CONDITION" ...AND THAT BLANQUE HAS CLASSIFIED THE ROBOT AS A **FUGITOID**, TO BE CAPTURED UNHARMED. IN THAT WAY, BLANQUE CAN EXPLOIT HONEYCUTT'S MIND, AND NO ONE WILL COMPLAIN -- FOR, AFTER ALL, ROBOTS HAVE NO RIGHTS!!!

A FEW HOURS LATER...

YOU SURE THIS IS THE RIGHT WAY?

YES... MY SENSORS "SMELL" SALT WATER... AND THE SPACEPORT IS NEAR THE SEAPORT.

ANY TROOPS?

LOOKS CLEAR-- LETS GO!

WHAT A DRAG... HERE WE ARE IN A CITY FULL OF FUNKY-LOOKING ALIENS...

WHY IS THAT BAD?

gleep?

IT'S NOT! SEE, ON EARTH WE HAVE TO HIDE BECAUSE WE'RE DIFFERENT... SO WE FINALLY GET TO A PLACE LIKE THIS WHERE WE CAN FIT RIGHT IN AND WHAT HAPPENS?-- WE HAVE TO HIDE OUT 'CUZ WE'RE AIDING AND ABETTING A FUGITIVE FROM THE LAW! YOU CAN'T WIN...

I GUESS NOT...

PORTNEROY'S SPACEPORT JOCKEY BAR

WATCH YOUR STEP

NO TOUR BOTS

HEY-- THIS BAR LOOKS PROMISING!

IT SHOULD SUFFICE...

64

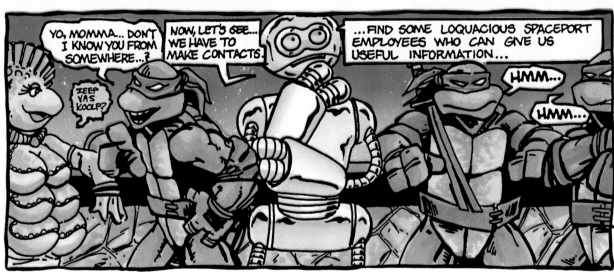

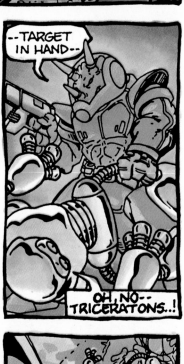

AH... THERE! I THINK I'VE GOT IT NOW, CAPTAIN!

VERY GOOD, MR. SCOTT! NOW TAKE US UP SO WE CAN SEE--

--THERE! ABOUT THREE MILES AHEAD--

--THOSE CREEPS THAT GRABBED HONEYCUTT!

LET'S GET 'EM!

YEAH, DON -- AS "THE BOSS" WOULD SAY: "STAND ON IT!"

CRANK THIS SUCKER!

A FEW MILES AHEAD, AND DIRECTLY IN THE TURTLES' FLIGHT PATH...

YOU HEAR AN ENGINE...?

YEAH... A CLUNKER, BUT COMING FAST... SOME FOOL FOLLOWING US...?

COULD BE NOTHING... COULD BE FEDERAT SOLDIERS...

WAIT 'TIL IT PASSES OVER...

ALRIGHT-- LET'S DO OUR REAR-GUARD THING!

FAN OUT IN ATTACK FORMATION --!

UH-OH... BAD COMPANY!

GOOD THING I'VE STILL GOT THIS BLASTER!

75

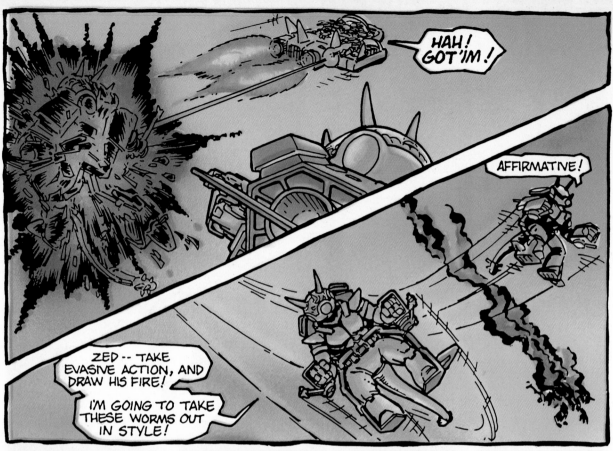

HAH! GOT 'IM!

AFFIRMATIVE!

ZED -- TAKE EVASIVE ACTION, AND DRAW HIS FIRE!

I'M GOING TO TAKE THESE WORMS OUT IN STYLE!

THAT OLD RUST-BUCKET SHOULDN'T EVEN BE IN THE AIR...

...SO, IN A WAY, I'M DOING YOU GEEKS...

...A BIG FAVOR!

YOU OK, LEO...?

OW-- YEAH! A LITTLE SORE...

IS EVERYBODY ELSE OK..?

DON? DON-- ARE YOU ALL RIGHT?

NO-- NO, I'M NOT! IT'S OVER, ISN'T IT? WITH HONEYCUTT GONE WE'RE STUCK HERE FOR GOOD!

ON TOP OF BEING MILLIONS OF MILES FROM HOME, WE'RE LOST IN THESE WOODS--

-- NO WAY OF KNOWING WHICH WAY THOSE HORN-HEADS WENT!

FINE! GIVE UP IF YOU WANT TO! NOT ME; I'M GOING HOME FOR SURE!

CALM DOWN RAPH-AEL!

DON'T WORRY, BROTHER-- WE'LL FIND A WAY BACK HOME SOMEHOW-- EH?

THAT NOISE?--

LOOK! FEDERATION TROOPSHIPS! THEY MUST BE HOT ON THE TRICERATON'S TRAIL!

WELL, WHAT ARE WE WAITING FOR?

THIS WAY-- LET'S GO!

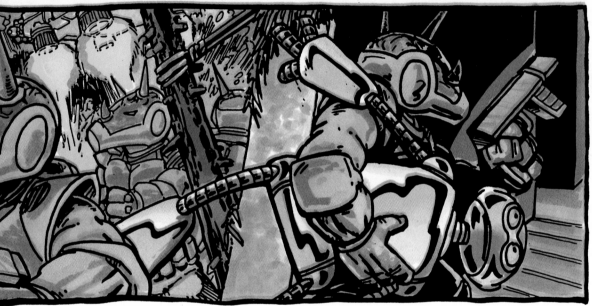

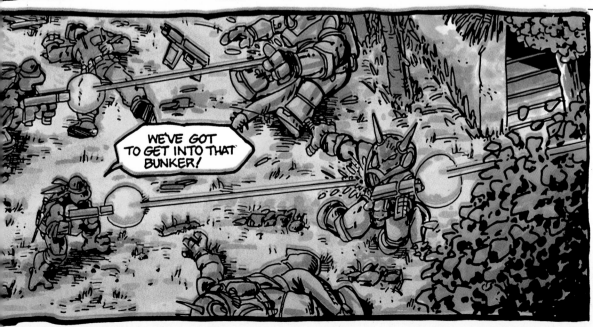

82

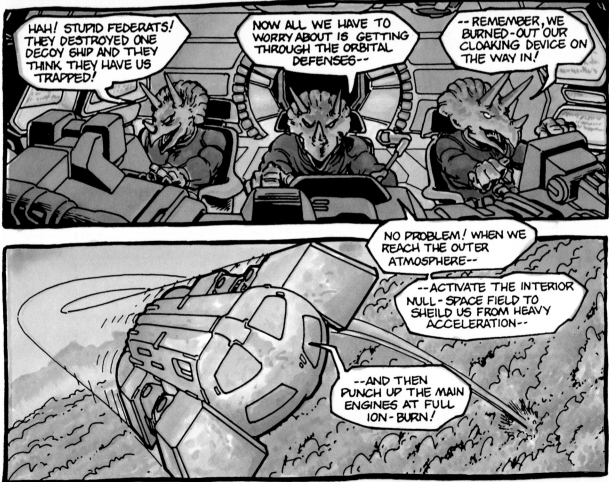

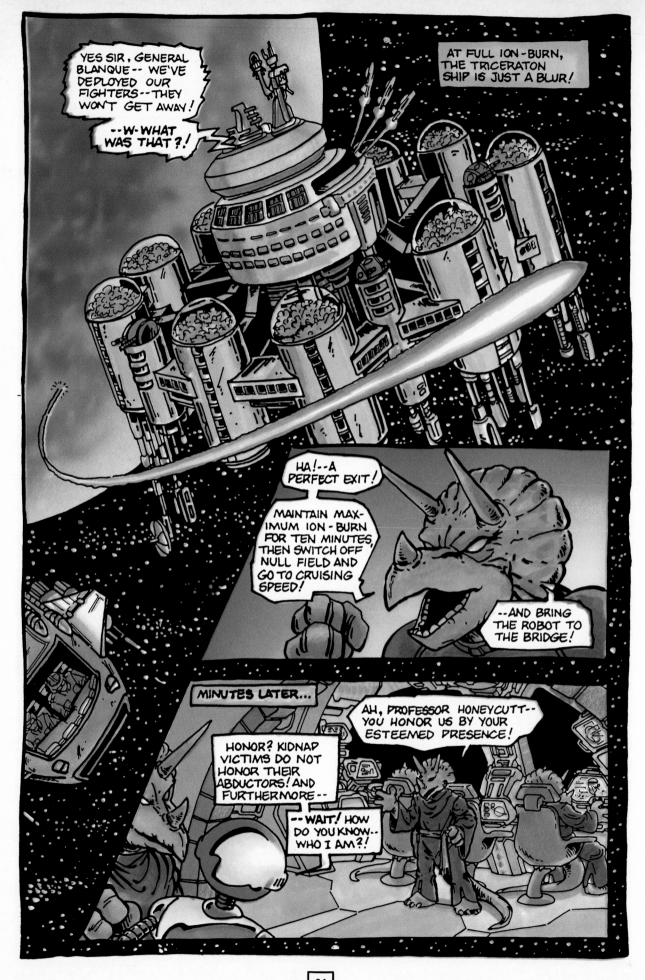

HAHAHA! SURPRISED? WE LEARNED YOUR IDENTITY FROM AN ASSOCIATE OF AN OLD FRIEND OF YOURS--

--GENERAL BLANQUE!

BLANQUE? THEN--HE KNEW... ALL THIS TIME...!

YES, HE KNEW... THAT THE SECRET OF THE ULTIMATE WEAPON WAS NOW LOCKED WITHIN THIS COMMON ROBOT'S BODY--

--AND WITHIN YOUR MIND! I SPEAK, OF COURSE--

--OF THE TRANSMAT DEVICE!

BUT--BUT I NEVER EVEN BUILT A PROTOTYPE! I DON'T KNOW IF IT WILL WORK--!

OH, DON'T BE SO MODEST, HONEYCUTT-- WE HAVE GREAT FAITH IN YOU!

SIR--! WE'VE JUST DROPPED OUT OF CRUISE MODE... ...BASE ONE IS JUST AHEAD!

VERY GOOD... SOON, HONEYCUTT, YOU WILL SEE THAT THE TRICERATON REPUBLIC HAS VAST RESOURCES FOR YOU TO EMPLOY IN YOUR CREATION OF THE TRANSMAT...

SIR? FUEL SUPPLY IS EXHAUSTED... WE'RE COASTING NOW... BASE ONE HAS LOCKED ONTO US... DOCKING ESTIMATED IN FIVE MINUTES!

NOW, PROFESSOR-- LOOK UPON ONE SMALL PART OF THE GLORY OF THE REPUBLIC--

GOOD HEAVEN-!!!

PROFESSOR HONEYCUTT IS SPEECHLESS. AHEAD LIES THE TRICERATON BASE -- A MOBILE MOUNTAIN!

ORIGINALLY AN ASTEROID, ITS SURFACE MELTED AND HARDENED BY CLOSE EXPOSURE TO A SUN... THE INTERIOR HOLLOWED OUT, AN ENTIRE CITY BUILT WITHIN...

...KILOMETER LONG DOCKING JETTIES JUT FROM IT'S SIDES... AND MASSIVE ION-DRIVE ENGINES BUILT RIGHT INTO THE ASTEROID'S ROCKY HEART, WAIT TO PROPEL IT THROUGH THE VOID OF SPACE!

MEAN WHILE, IN A CARGO HOLD...

:COUGH:

SO... :COUGH: ..THIS IS WHAT ZERO GRAVITY FEELS LIKE!

OK, ENOUGH :COUGH: FOOLING AROUND! LET'S GO :COUGH: FIND HONEYCUTT!

HEY... AH, GUYS? :COUGH: IS IT ME, OR IS IT :COUGH: GETTING HARD TO BREATHE?

AH, PROFESSOR HONEYCUTT! I'M PLEASED THAT YOU HAVE DECIDED TO JOIN US ON THE COMMAND DECK!

WELL, I WOULD LIKE TO SEE WHERE WE'RE GOING... ...NOT THAT I HAVE ANY CHOICE IN THE MATTER!

HAH, HAH! VERY GOOD, HONEYCUTT-- YOU TRY TO DISGUISE YOUR CURIOSITY BENEATH A VENEER OF CYNICISM. BUT I KNOW THAT, AS A SCIENTIST, YOU ARE FASCINATED BY OUR TECHNOLOGY!

HMMPH! I DO CONFESS TO SOME INTEREST... BUT LESS IN THE TECHNOLOGY AND MORE IN ITS APPLICATION!

SLOWING TO DOCKING SPEED, SIR... VISUAL IN FIVE SECONDS...

YES, OUR **ASTEROID SHIPS** ALWAYS MAKE A GOOD IMPRESSION. HOWEVER, A WIDELY-KNOWLEGEABLE BEING SUCH AS YOURSELF WOULD NOT BE REALLY STARTLED BY ANYTHING LESS THAN WHAT AWAITS US BEYOND THIS PLANET WHICH WE ARE NOW COMING AROUND...

"DOCKING SPEED"... WHERE COULD YOU POSSIBLY DOCK SOMETHING THIS **HUGE**?!

HAH! SEE FOR YOURSELF, PROFESSOR! LOOK UPON--

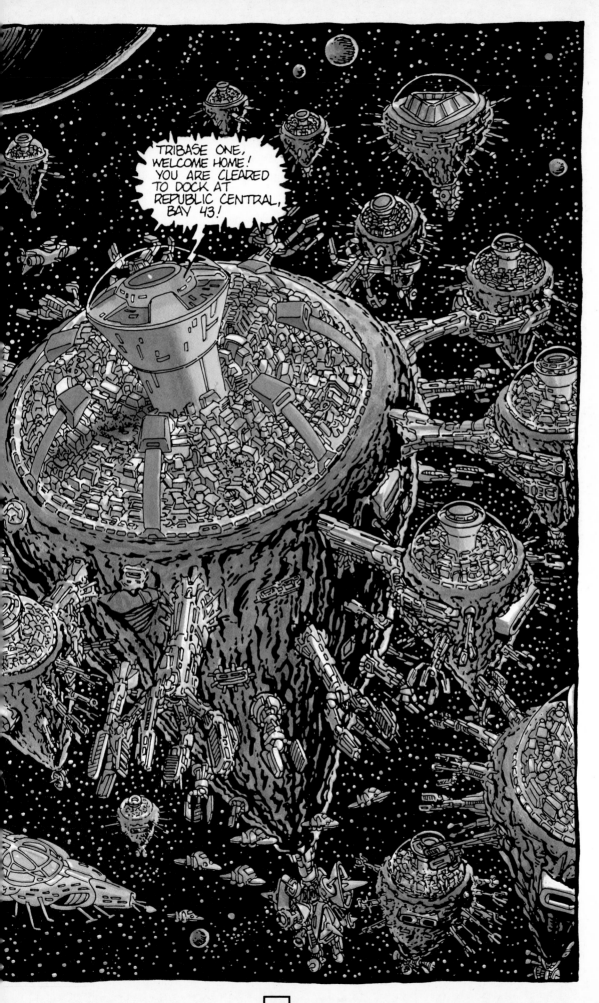

MEANWHILE, BACK AT TRIBASE ONE, THE SCOUT SHIP USED TO KIDNAP HONEYCUTT IS BEING INSPECTED AND REPAIRED...

I WANT THAT SHIP FULLY REFUELED AND RECHARGED... CHECK EVERY INCH FOR DAMAGE... INVENTORY ALL SUPPLIES...

...AND DISINFECT IT! WHO KNOWS WHAT FOUL DISEASES IT MIGHT HAVE PICKED UP ON THAT FEDERAT PLANET!

...AND IN A LOWER HOLD...

HMM... STRANGE PLACE FOR BLASTER BURNS...

...I DIDN'T THINK THAT THE FIGHT WITH THE FEDERATS GOT THIS FAR INSIDE THE SHIP!

YOU TROOPS, CHECK THIS ROOM OUT-- THOROUGHLY!

SEEMS EMPTY TO ME...

WAIT-- LOOK!

WHAT ARE THEY?

ARE THEY-- DEAD?

LOOKS LIKE WE HAVE SOME STOWAWAYS HERE... CAN'T PLACE THE SPECIES... THEY SEEM TO BE IN SOME KIND OF TRANCE! IF WE PICKED THEM UP ON D'HOONIB, THEY'RE PROBABLY OXYGEN BREATHERS-- BETTER GET SOME ATMOSPHERE CONVERTORS QUICKLY!

YA KNOW, PINHEAD, BACK WHERE I COME FROM, BOZOS LIKE YOU KNOW THEIR PLACE...

...IN MUSEUMS, DISPLAYED AS SKELETONS OF LONG-DEAD ANCIENT FREAKS!

WHY YOU--! I OUGHTA--!

URRR--!

LOOK AT THIS *JERK* BROTHERS-- BIG, SLOW, AND CLUMSY!

HAI!

YEAH, BUT THEY'RE TOO CHICKEN TO USE 'EM!

OUFF!

NO, MIKE-- THEY'VE GOT GUNS!

HAIYAA! REMEMBER WHAT THE *HEAD LIZARD* SAID?

FOR SOME REASON, THEY WANT US-- KIAI!

ARR!

WHUF!

--UNHARMED! YAIHA!

WELL, ALL RIGHT! THIS ONE'S GOT SOME SPUNK! I LIKE THAT... SO WHEN THE TIME COMES, I'M GOING TO KILL YOU FIRST!

BUT ENOUGH FUN...

OW!

...NOW GET INSIDE!

...THE REST OF YOU, TOO!

YOU O.K., MIKE?

YEAH...

LATER, CHUMPS! LOCK IT UP, BOYS!

...TRAPPED BY ANOTHER POWER-HUNGRY, BLOODTHIRSTY BUREAUCRACY! THE TRICERATON REPUBLIC IS NO MORE OR LESS EVIL THAN THE HUMAN FEDERATION...

...BUT EACH IS JUST AS ETHNO-CENTRIC, XENOPHOBIC, AND PARANOID AS THE OTHER! NOW THE TRICERATONS WILL TRY TO FORCE ME TO BUILD THAT FRIGHTFUL WEAPON, THE TRANSMAT... AND I HAVE TO FACE THE HARD FACT THAT EVEN IF I CAN BUILD THE DEVICE, I WON'T... THE POTENTIAL FOR MASS DEATH AND PAIN AND TERROR IN THE GALAXY IS TOO GREAT... I JUST CAN'T DO IT... EVEN IF IT MEANS MY DEATH--AND THE DEATHS OF MY FOUR NEW FRIENDS!

ELSEWHERE...

WHAT A MESS THIS IS... IT SEEMS LIKE EVER SINCE MY MIND WAS ACCIDENTALLY LODGED INSIDE THIS ROBOT BODY, THINGS HAVE GONE FROM BAD TO WORSE!

FIRST, GENERAL BLANQUE CLAS-SIFIES ME AS A FUGITOID AND HUNTS ME DOWN WITH THE IN-TENTION OF EXTORTING FROM ME MY KNOWLEGE OF THE TRANSMAT...

...AND THEN THOSE TRICERATONS SHOW UP WITH THE SAME IDEA!

...AND THE TURTLES... THOSE GUYS JUST WANTED TO HELP ME OUT, AND GET BACK TO THEIR HOMEWORLD... AND I WAS GOING TO TRY TO HELP THEM DO THAT... BUT NOW LOOK WHERE WE ALL ARE!

SOME TRILLIONS OF LIGHT YEARS AWAY FROM A LONELY PROFESSOR CONTEMPLATING HIS DEATH, A SMALL SOLAR SYSTEM LIES... ITS ONLY KNOWN INHABITED PLANET, CALLED EARTH, IS THE THIRD WORLD ORBITING THE LIFE-GIVING SUN...

ON THIS PLANET ARE ARTIFICIAL SURFACE DIVISIONS CALLED NATIONS... ONE OF THE LARGEST AND MOST POWERFUL IS THE UNITED STATES OF AMERICA... THE NATIONS OF EARTH REFLECT, IN MICROCOSM, THE STRUGGLE BETWEEN...

...THE FEDERATS AND THE TRICERATONS... THOUGH THE PEOPLE OF EARTH KNOW NOTHING OF THAT DISTANT CONFLICT...

NEW YORK CITY, U.S.A... ...THE "BIG APPLE"... CITY OF LIGHTS, HOPES, DREAMS... AND VIOLENCE...

ON A SIDE STREET IN THAT CITY, THE "SECOND TIME AROUND" JUNK SHOP INHERITED AND RUN BY APRIL O'NEIL...

...A YOUNG WOMAN NOW VERY WORRIED, DUE TO THE TWO-DAY ABSENCE OF FOUR GREEN ADOLESCENT WARRIOR REPTILES...

OH, PLEASE...

OH, GREAT-- "THE MUNSTERS"! JUST WHAT I NEED TO CHEER ME UP...!

HERMAN, DEAR, GRANDA'S RIGHT-- EDDIE'S A BIG WEREWOLF NOW AND SHOULDN'T BULLY THE OTHER KIDS AT SCHOOL!

NOW LILLY, I'M HIS FATHER, AND--

HUH?

WE INTERRUPT THIS PROGRAM TO BRING YOU ANOTHER LIVE EYEWITNESS NEWS REPORT FROM DOWNTOWN BROOKLYN. JIM...?

THANKS, BOB! JIM McNAUGHTON HERE, COMING TO YOU LIVE FROM THE SITE OF THE MYSTERIOUS T.C.R.I. BUILDING, THE OBJECT OF INTENSE OFFICIAL SCRUTINY SINCE APPROXIMATELY 9:30 P.M. TWO NIGHTS AGO, WHEN MANY WITNESSES OBSERVED A BLINDING BEAM OF LIGHT WHICH BURST FROM THE TOP OF THE STRUCTURE--

--AND SHOT MILES INTO THE NEW YORK SKY. SINCE THEN, THERE HAS BEEN NO RESPONSE FROM T.C.R.I. OFFICIALS, AND NO ONE HAS BEEN ALLOWED ENTRANCE INTO THE BUILDING. OUR RESEARCH STAFF HAS BEEN UNABLE TO FIND OUT WHAT IT IS THAT THE T.C.R.I. COMPANY DOES...

T.C.R.I.?!! OH MY GOD-- THAT'S WHERE THE GUYS WERE HEADED WHEN THEY LEFT TWO DAYS AGO--!

SMASH

...ALL WE KNOW SO FAR IS WHAT THE INITIALS T.C.R.I. STAND FOR: "TECHNO-COSMIC RESEARCH INSTITUTE." NOW, WITH THE LATEST DEVELOPMENTS, HERE'S CAPTAIN FARRILLO OF THE N.Y.P.D. WHAT'S THE SCOOP, CAPTAIN?

OH, NO...

WELL, ABOUT TWENTY MINUTES AGO, AFTER REPEATED -- AND UN-SUCCESSFUL -- ATTEMPTS TO CONTACT T.C.R.I. OFFICIALS, WE DECIDED TO TRY TO FORCE ENTRY. AS OUR OFFICERS PREPARED TO BREAK THROUGH THE GLASS MAIN DOORS, SOLID STEEL PLATES EJECTED FROM ALL THE DOOR AND WINDOW FRAMES, SEALING THE BUILDING COMPLETELY. EVEN THE ROOFTOP ENTRYWAY WAS SEALED OFF.

SO WHAT'S NEXT?

WELL, THE MAYOR PLANS TO CALL IN THE NATIONAL GUARD AND TRY ANOTHER FORCED ENTRY. UNTIL THEN, WE'LL KEEP TRYING TO CONTACT WHOEVER IS INSIDE THE BUILDING... AND TO FIND OUT WHO OWNS THE DARN PLACE!

THANKS, CAPTAIN FARRILLO! I GUESS THAT WRAPS IT UP FOR NOW.

WE'LL HAVE MORE REPORTS ON THIS SITUATION AS IT EVOLVES. COMING TO YOU LIVE FROM BROOKLYN, THIS IS JIM McNAUGHTON, EYEWITNESS NEWS!

OH, GEEZ-- THE GUYS! WHAT'S HAPPENED TO THEM? IF THEY'RE TRAPPED INSIDE THAT BUILDING, THEY'LL BE CAUGHT--! WHAT SHOULD I DO?

WHAT CAN I DO?

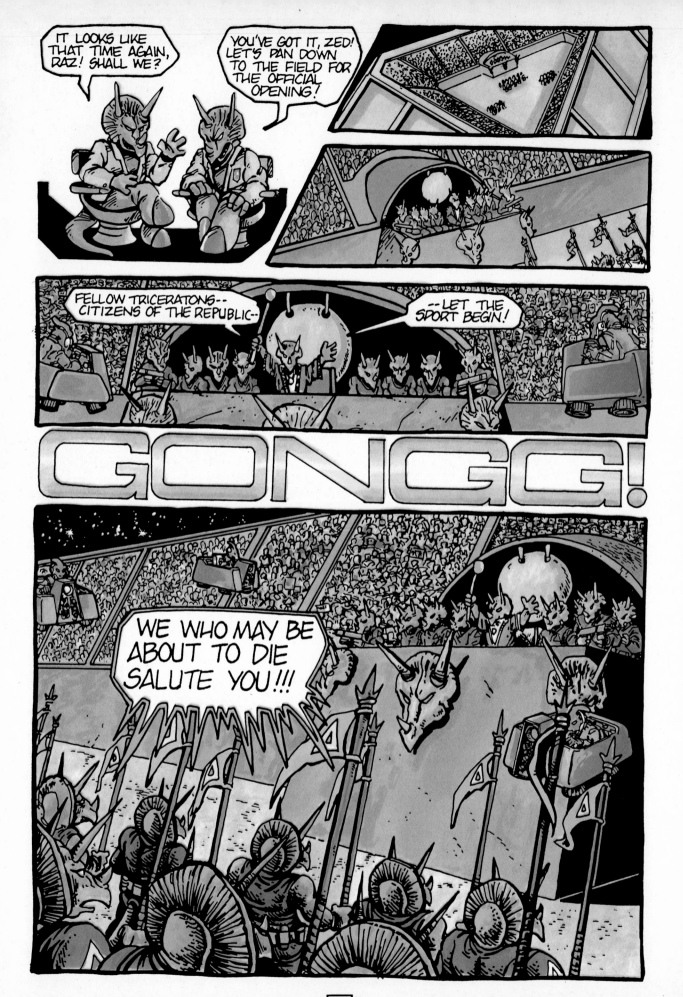

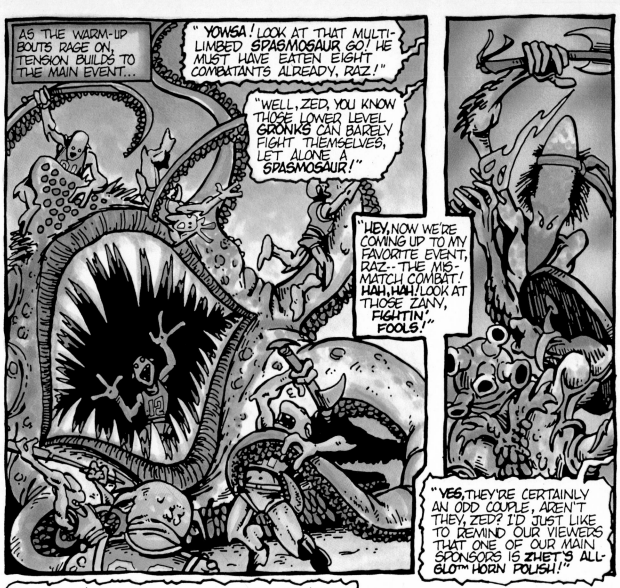

AS THE WARM-UP BOUTS RAGE ON, TENSION BUILDS TO THE MAIN EVENT...

"YOWSA! LOOK AT THAT MULTI-LIMBED *SPASMOSAUR* GO! HE MUST HAVE EATEN EIGHT COMBATANTS ALREADY, RAZ!"

"WELL, ZED, YOU KNOW THOSE LOWER LEVEL *GRONKS* CAN BARELY FIGHT THEMSELVES, LET ALONE A *SPASMOSAUR!*"

"HEY, NOW WE'RE COMING UP TO MY FAVORITE EVENT, RAZ-- THE MIS-MATCH COMBAT! HAH, HAH! LOOK AT THOSE ZANY, FIGHTIN' FOOLS!"

"YES, THEY'RE CERTAINLY AN ODD COUPLE, AREN'T THEY, ZED? I'D JUST LIKE TO REMIND OUR VIEWERS THAT ONE OF OUR MAIN SPONSORS IS *ZHET'S* ALL-GLO™ HORN POLISH!"

"ALL *RIGHT!* IT'S THE ALL-OUT GANG WAR, AND WHAT A WAR IT IS, RAZ! LOOK AT THOSE CRAZIES GO-- BLOOD 'N' GUTS EVERYWHERE! I DEFINITELY FAVOR THE *TROGS* THIS TIME OUT-- THEY'VE REALLY GOT THEIR STUFF TOGETHER!"

"GOT TO DISAGREE WITH YOU THERE, ZED-- THE *NOIDS* HAVE A DYNAMITE BACKFIELD, AND THEIR CENTERS ARE REALLY TAKING OFF HEADS IN THE FIRST QUARTER!"

IT'S ALMOST TIME... BRING HONEYCUTT OUT NOW...

AT ONCE, PRIME LEADER!

WHAT AN INCREDIBLE MOVE! DO WE HAVE INSTANT REPLAY ON THAT, RAZ?

THERE IT IS, ZED-- WHAT A MOVE BY #66, LAK NIEPUR OUT OF ZAL STATE. LOOK AT THE WAY HE HANDLES THAT TRIPLE-BLADED AXE ON THAT *DISEMBOWELMENT!* WELL, SPORTS FANS, WE ARE JUST MOMENTS AWAY FROM THE *MAIN EVENT--* SO WE'LL PAUSE FOR STATION IDENTIFICATION AND A WORD FROM ONE OF OUR SPONSORS, NICK'S SPACE JOOZ™: THE SWILL OF CHAMPIONS!!!

AH, HONEYCUTT... YOU'RE JUST IN TIME--

--WE'VE ARRANGED THIS NEXT EVENT ESPECIALLY FOR YOU!

WITH ALL DUE RESPECT, PRIME LEADER ZANRAMON, I CARE VERY LITTLE ABOUT SPORTS --AND WHAT I'VE HEARD ABOUT YOUR *BLOODY GAMES* SICKENS ME!

PERHAPS... BUT THIS NEXT BOUT WILL AT LEAST INTEREST YOU, BELIEVE ME!

FELLOW SAURIANS! -- SPORTS FANS OF ALL SPECIES! -- YOUR ATTENTION, PLEASE! THIS IS IT -- THE ONE YOU'VE BEEN WAITING FOR-- THE BIG EVENT OF THIS TOURNAMENT!

IN THE CENTER OF THE ARENA, NOW EXITING THE PLAYER TRANSPORT MODULE, ALLOW ME TO INTRODUCE--

THIS IS INSANE! THEY'VE DONE NOTHING WRONG-- THEY DON'T DESERVE TO BE SACRIFICED IN YOUR *HORROR SHOW!*

AH, HONEYCUTT... IT IS YOUR *STUBBORN-NESS* WHICH FORCES THIS... SITUATION. SAY THAT YOU WILL *BUILD* A TRANS-MAT FOR US, AND YOUR FRIENDS WILL NOT BE HARMED!

I KNEW IT-- I KNEW YOU'D TRY SOME-THING LIKE THIS! EVEN SO, I FIND IT HARD TO BELIEVE YOU COULD BE SO *CRUEL!* I'LL NEVER BUILD YOUR *DAMNED* MACHINE, YOU *REPTILIAN BASTARD*-- *NEVER!!!*

HAVE IT YOUR WAY, FOOL! IT'S TOO BAD ABOUT YOUR FRIENDS-- THEY'RE SURE TO DIE! HAH, HAH, HAH!

THIS IS IT, MY BROTHERS-- THESE GUYS ARE *BIG, MEAN*... AND *VETERANS* OF THIS SO-CALLED *SPORT!* EVEN IF WE WIN, WHO KNOWS WHAT THESE HORN-HEADED CREEPS WILL DO TO US NEXT?!

DON'T WORRY, LEO-- SPLINTER TAUGHT US TO LIVE AND DIE WITH HONOR... AND WE WILL!

DAMN STRAIGHT--!

--I'VE HAD JUST ABOUT AS MUCH AS I'LL TAKE FROM THESE PRE-HISTORIC DUKES! PUSH US AROUND-- *GRRRR!* I'M GONNA KILL THEM ALL MYSELF!!!

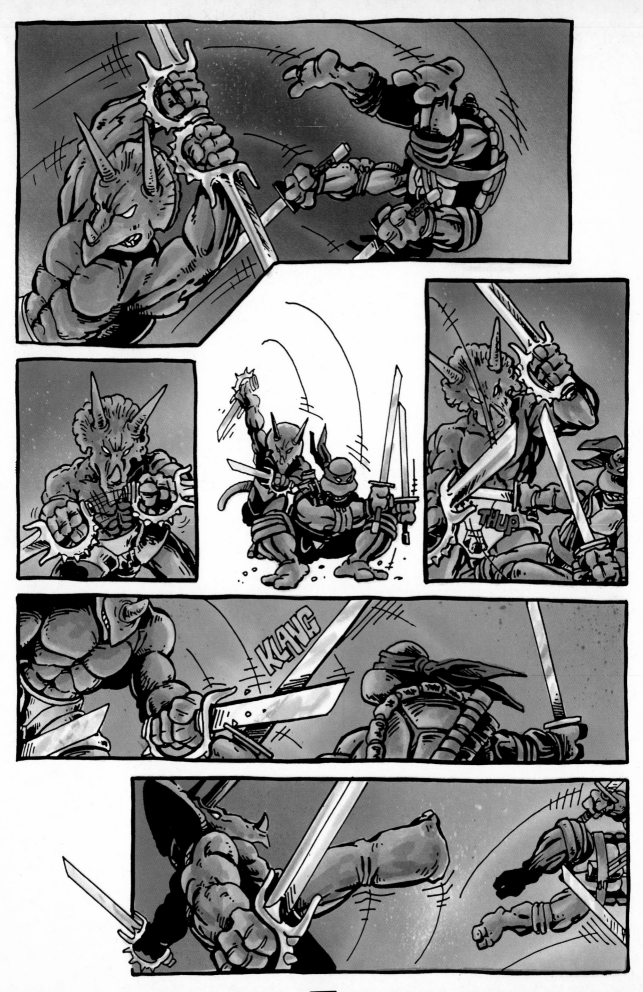

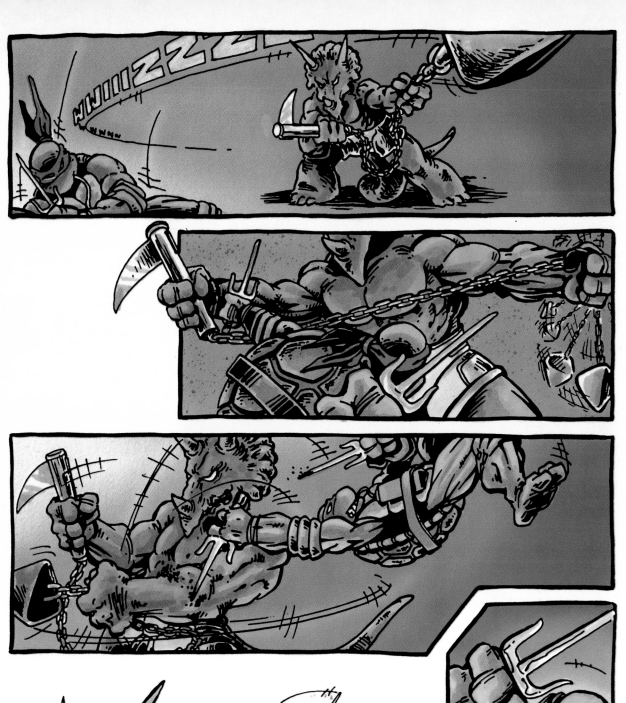

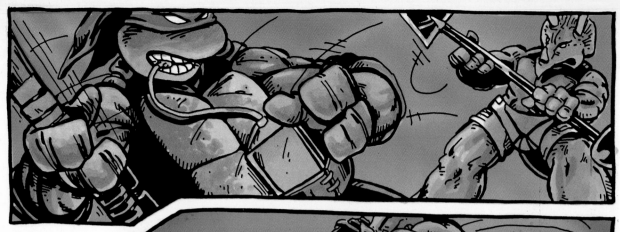

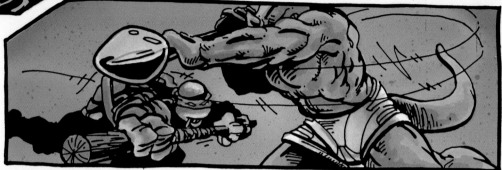

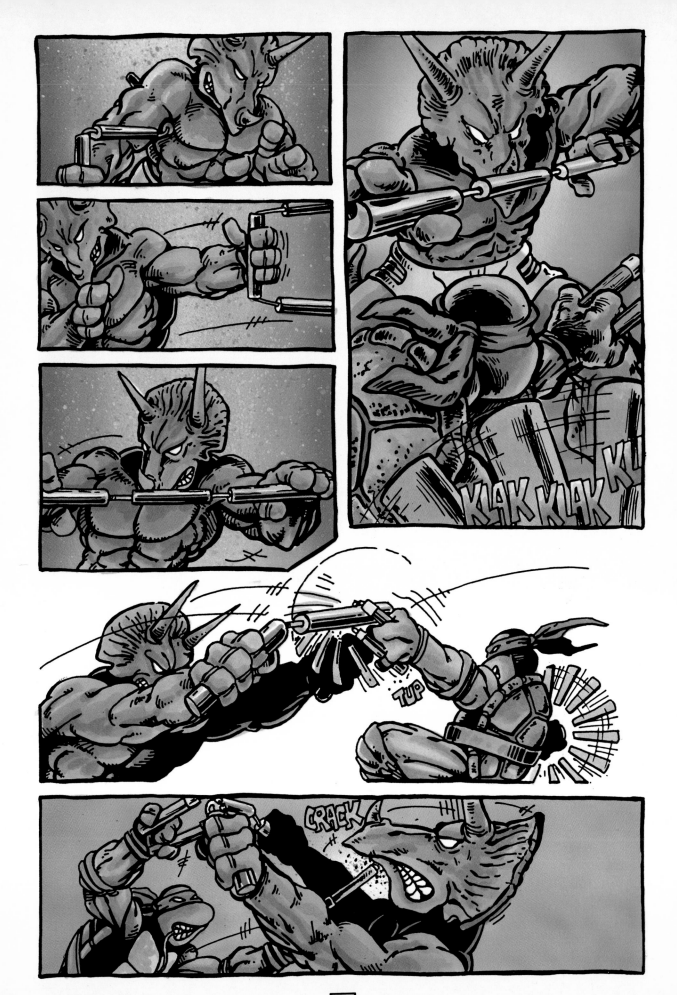

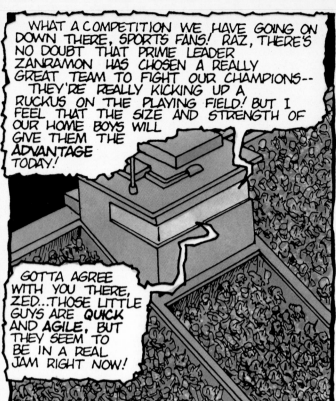

WHAT A COMPETITION WE HAVE GOING ON DOWN THERE, SPORTS FANS! RAZ, THERE'S NO DOUBT THAT PRIME LEADER ZANRAMON HAS CHOSEN A REALLY GREAT TEAM TO FIGHT OUR CHAMPIONS-- THEY'RE REALLY KICKING UP A RUCKUS ON THE PLAYING FIELD! BUT I FEEL THAT THE SIZE AND STRENGTH OF OUR HOME BOYS WILL GIVE THEM THE ADVANTAGE TODAY!

GOTTA AGREE WITH YOU THERE, ZED...THOSE LITTLE GUYS ARE QUICK AND AGILE, BUT THEY SEEM TO BE IN A REAL JAM RIGHT NOW!

WOW! LOOK AT THAT! WHAT A GREAT MOVE BY THAT TURTLE! HIS TEAM IS THE FIRST TO REACH THE SCORE BOARD, WITH A ONE-POINT ADVANTAGE!

RAZ, THE FANS ARE GOING WILD! **I CAN'T BELIEVE IT--** THAT'S TWO IN A ROW FOR THE **TURTLES!** COULD IT BE BEGINNERS' LUCK? ARE OUR BOYS OVERCONFIDENT? I DON'T KNOW... BUT I HOPE THE CAMERA CREWS ARE GETTING **CLOSE-UPS--** THESE GUYS ARE GOOD!!!

FOR HONOR--!

DON--ARE YOU OKAY?!

LEO, LOOK--UP ON THAT PLATFORM--

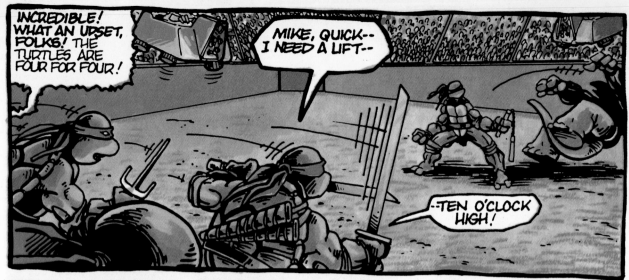

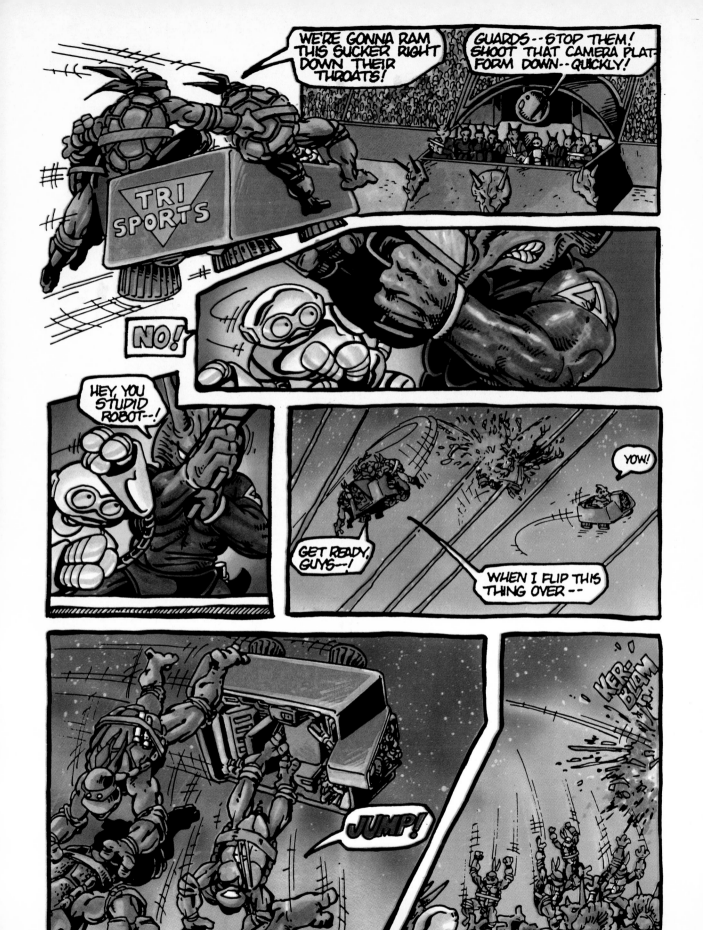

NAIL THOSE GUARDS, AND GRAB HONEYCUTT--

--I SEE OUR TICKET OUT OF HERE!

PRIME LEADER, MAKE ONE MOVE AND YOU'RE LIZARD CUTLETS! CALL OFF YOUR GUARDS--

NOW!!!

AHHH--!!

Y-YOU HEARD HIM--BACK OFF! GIVE HIM ROOM! DON'T *GULP* SHOOT!

OH MY GOD...! FANS AND FELLOW TRICERATONS... OH MY GOD! THE COMBATANTS-- THOSE TURTLES HAVE ATTACKED AND NOW HOLD PRISONER OUR PRIME LEADER--! OH MY GOD--! THIS IS TERRIBLE, HORRIFYING...

...CAMERA SIX, CAN YOU GET A CLOSE UP OF THE ACTION?

OKAY, PAL-- YOU JUST HELP US GET OUT OF HERE, AND WE'LL TURN YOU LOOSE UNHARMED!

BROTHERS, GRAB SOME WEAPONS, AND BE READY FOR ANYTHING...I DON'T TRUST THESE CREEPS!

LOOK, YOU UGLY HUNK OF SNOT, WE'RE NOT FOOLING AROUND! YOU'D BETTER CALL YOUR GOONS OFF REAL QUICK OR YOU'RE *HISTORY!*

DON'T SHOOT! HOLD YOUR FIRE AND PULL BACK! I, YOUR PRIME LEADER, ORDER YOU!

NEARBY...

GENERAL ZHATH, THE TERRORISTS ARE NOW IN THE ACCESS CORRIDOR TO THE PRIME LEADER'S PRIVATE HANGER...

THEY'LL HAVE TO COME DOWN THE CORRIDOR, EMERGING INTO THIS OPEN SPACE, WHICH THEY'LL HAVE TO CROSS TO GET TO THE PRIME LEADER'S SHIP. WE CAN POSITION SNIPERS AMONG THE MACHINERY IN THE HANGAR BAY, AND TRY TO PICK OFF THE CRIMINALS WHEN THEY'RE IN THE OPEN.
ITS RISKY, BUT IT'S OUR ONLY CHANCE--!

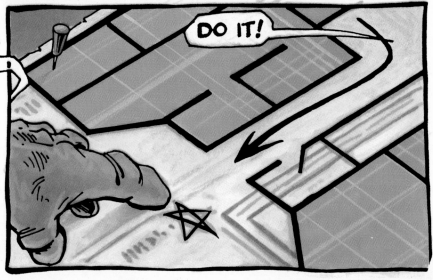

DO IT!